# GREAT BALLADS
## Playalong *for* Tenor Saxophone

M263

**Wise Publications**
part of The Music Sales Group
London/New York/Paris/Sydney/Copenhagen/Berlin/Madrid/Tokyo

Published by
**Wise Publications**
8/9 Frith Street, London W1D 3JB, England.

Exclusive Distributors:
**Music Sales Limited**
Distribution Centre, Newmarket Road, Bury St. Edmunds,
Suffolk IP33 3YB England.
**Music Sales Pty Limited**
120 Rothschild Avenue, Rosebery, NSW 2018, Australia.

Order No. AM978901
ISBN 1-84449-301-6
This book © Copyright 2004 by Wise Publications.

Compiled by Nick Crispin.
Music arranged by Simon Lesley.
Music processed by Paul Ewers Music Design.
Cover photography by George Taylor.
Printed in Great Britain.

CD recorded, mixed and mastered by Jonas Persson.
Instrumental solos by John Whelan.

Your Guarantee of Quality:
As publishers, we strive to produce every book to
the highest commercial standards.
The music has been freshly engraved and the book has been
carefully designed to minimise awkward page turns and
to make playing from it a real pleasure.
Particular care has been given to specifying acid-free, neutral-sized
paper made from pulps which have not been elemental chlorine bleached.
This pulp is from farmed sustainable forests and was
produced with special regard for the environment.
Throughout, the printing and binding have been planned to
ensure a sturdy, attractive publication which should give years of enjoyment.
If your copy fails to meet our high standards,
please inform us and we will gladly replace it.

**www.musicsales.com**

# Saxophone Fingering Chart

LIGATURE

**MOUTHPIECE**

**CROOK**

THUMB SUPPORT

**BODY**

1L
4L

2L
3L
**1ST FINGER**
5L
**2ND FINGER**
**3RD FINGER**
6L
7L
8L
9L

**LEFT HAND**

OCTAVE KEY
THUMB REST

1R
2R
3R
*4R
**1ST FINGER**
5R
**2ND FINGER**
**3RD FINGER**
6R
7R

**RIGHT HAND**

THE RING

* Not fitted on some saxophones

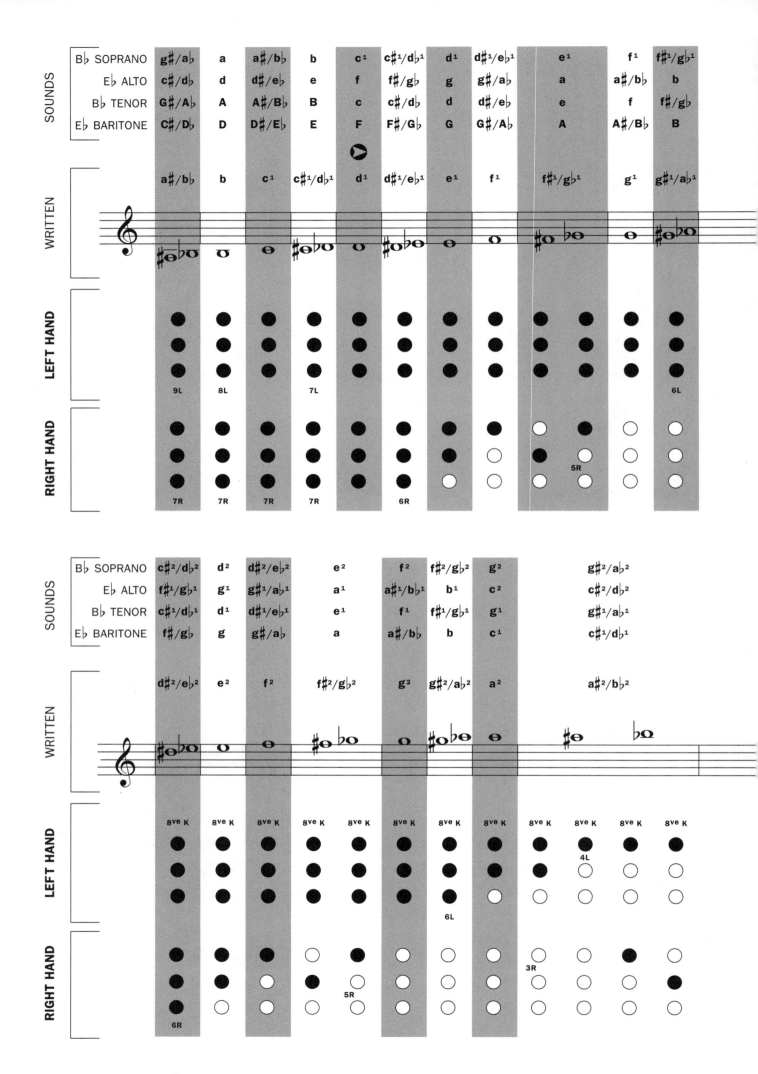

Indicates the lower limit of the best playing range

Indicates the upper limit of the best playing range

# Against All Odds (Take A Look At Me Now)

Words & Music by Phil Collins

**Dramatic ballad** ♩ = 58

6

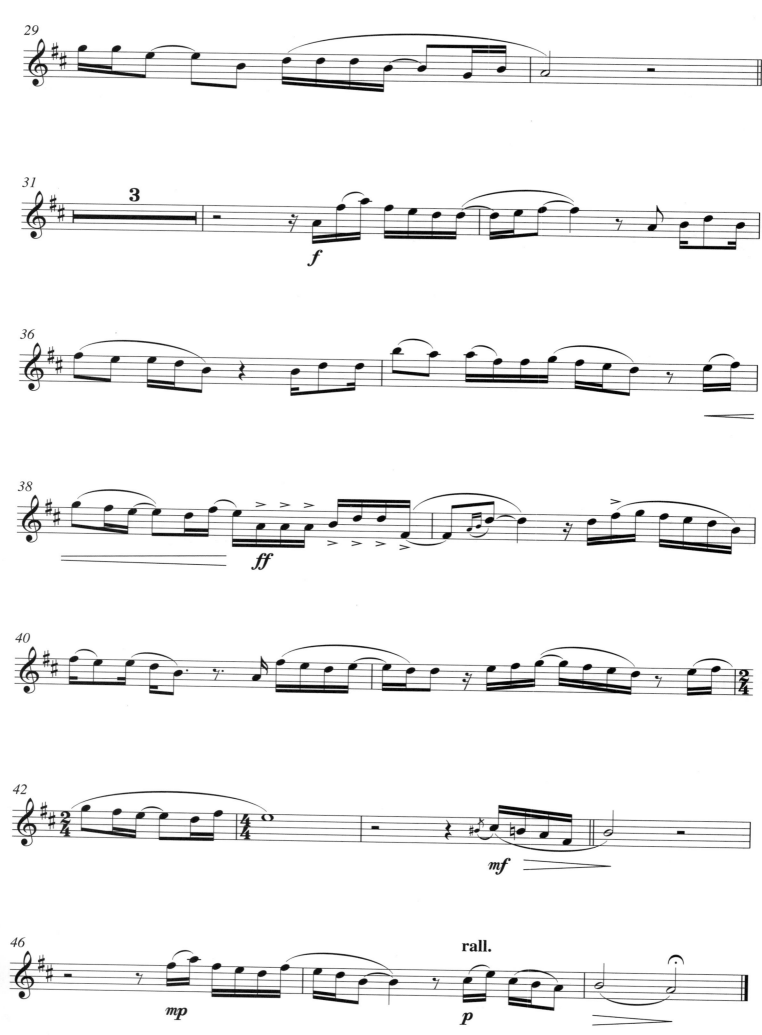

# Have I Told You Lately

**Words & Music by Van Morrison**

**Tenderly** ♩ = c.72

cue: play if desired

# How Deep Is Your Love

Words & Music by Barry Gibb, Maurice Gibb & Robin Gibb

**Moderate soft rock beat** ♩ = 105

electric pno. cue:

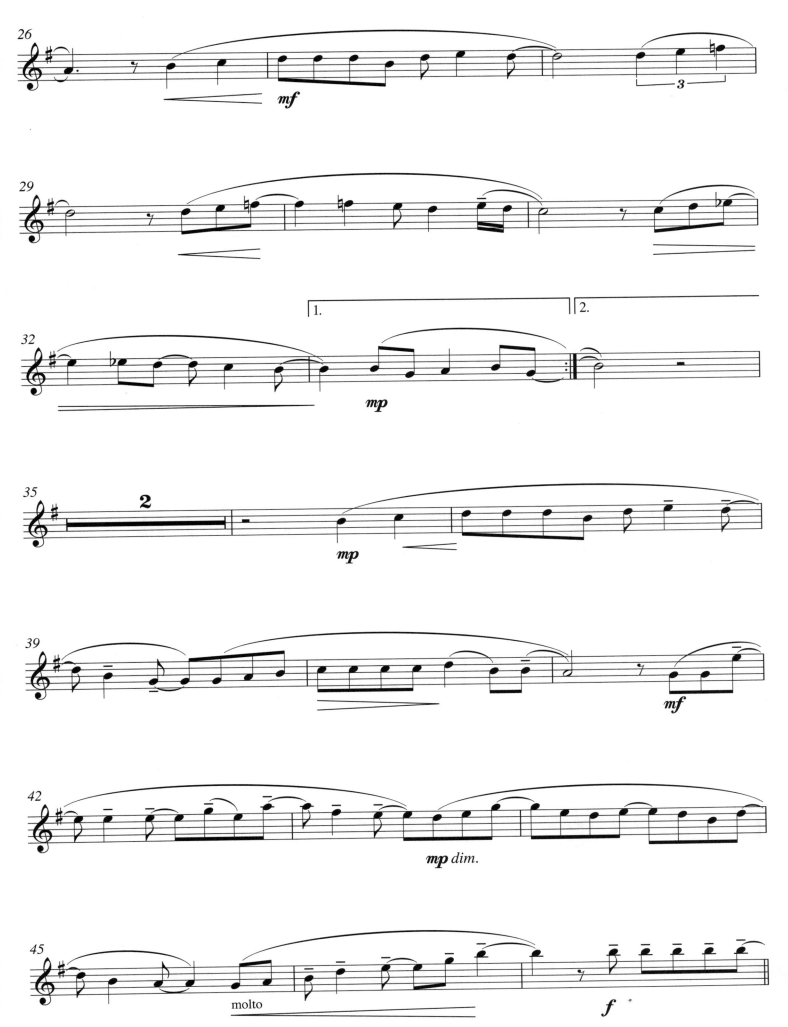

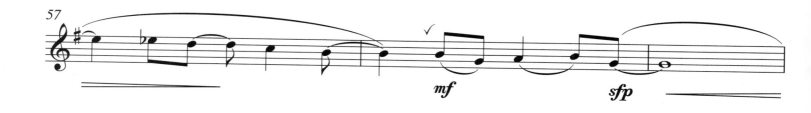

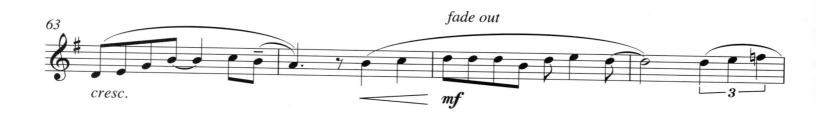

# If Tomorrow Never Comes

**Words & Music by Garth Brooks & Kent Blazy**

**Soft country-rock ballad** ♩ = 80

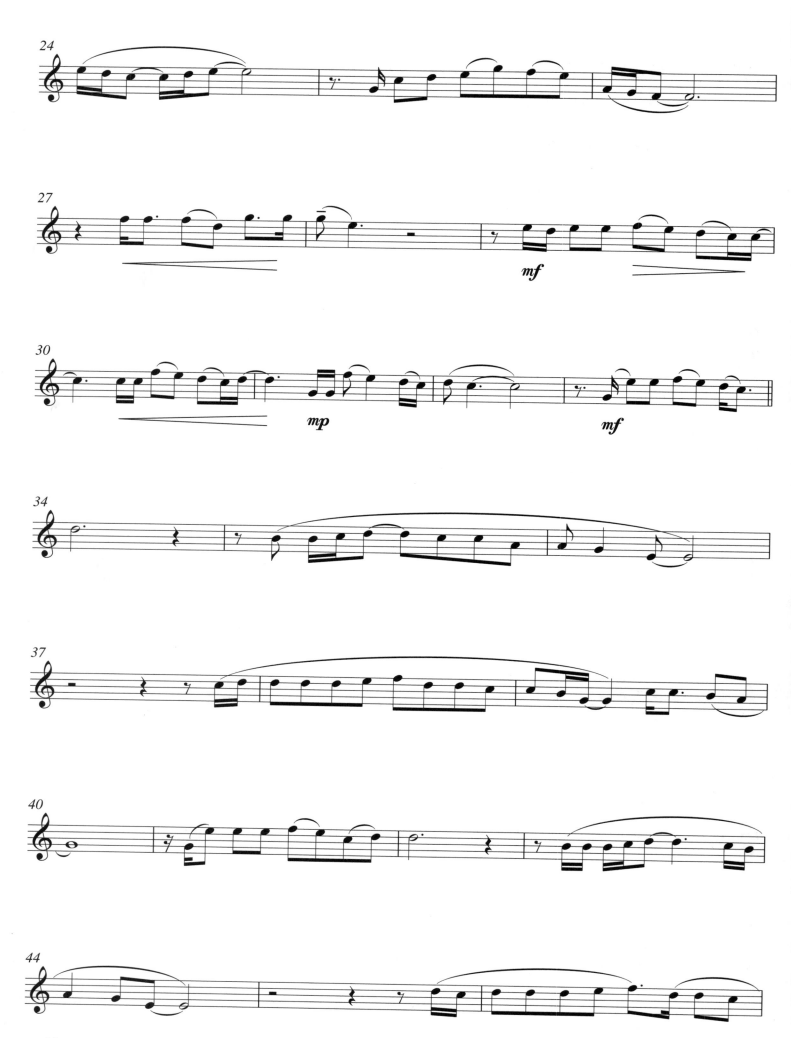

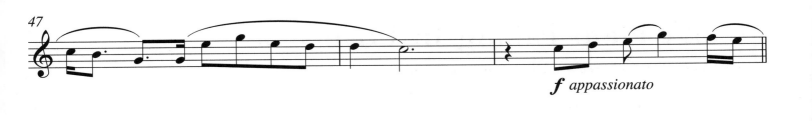

# Can't Help Falling In Love

Words & Music by George David Weiss, Hugo Peretti & Luigi Creatore

**In a slow 50s style** ♩· = 68

*mp molto legato e espr.*

# The Air That I Breathe

Words & Music by Albert Hammond & Mike Hazlewood

**Moderately**

# Nothing Compares 2 U

Words & Music by Prince

**Atmospheric and slightly funky, with hip-hop ♪s ♩ = 60**

# Time After Time

Words & Music by Cyndi Lauper & Robert Hyman

# Tonight

Words & Music by Steve Mac, Wayne Hector & Jörgen Elofsson

**Sadly, in a rock style** ♩ = 67

# Your Song

Words & Music by Elton John & Bernie Taupin

**Slow, but with a beat** ♩ = 64

**CD Track Listing**

1. Tuning notes

**Full instrumental performances...**

2. Against All Odds
   (Take A Look At Me Now)
   (Collins) Hit & Run Music (Publishing) Limited

3. Have I Told You Lately
   (Morrison) Universal Music Publishing Limited

4. How Deep Is Your Love
   (B.Gibb/M.Gibb/R.Gibb) BMG Music Publishing Limited

5. If Tomorrow Never Comes
   (Brooks/Blazy) BMG Music Publishing Limited /
   Hornall Brothers Music Limited

6. Can't Help Falling In Love
   (Weiss/Peretti/Creatore) Manor Music Company Limited

7. The Air That I Breathe
   (Hammond/Hazlewood) Rondor Music (London) Limited.

8. Nothing Compares 2 U
   (Prince) Universal/MCA Music Limited

9. Time After Time
   (Lauper/Hyman) Warner/Chappell Music Limited /
   Sony/ATV Music Publishing (UK) Limited

10. Tonight
    (Mac/Hector/Elofsson) Rokstone Music / Universal Music Publishing Limited /
    BMG Music Publishing Limited

11. Your Song
    (John/Taupin) Universal/Dick James Music Limited

**Backing tracks only...**

12. Against All Odds
    (Take A Look At Me Now)

13. Have I Told You Lately

14. How Deep Is Your Love

15. If Tomorrow Never Comes

16. Can't Help Falling In Love

17. The Air That I Breathe

18. Nothing Compares 2 U

19. Time After Time

20. Tonight

21. Your Song

MCPS

To remove your CD from the plastic sleeve, lift the
small lip on the right to break the perforated flap.
Replace the disc after use for convenient storage.